CONTENTS

Amazing Grace
by Mary Hoffman and Caroline Binch

CREDITS

Published by Scholastic Ltd,
Villiers House,
Clarendon Avenue,
Leamington Spa,
Warwickshire CV32 5PR
Text © Judith Graham
© 1997 Scholastic Ltd
    4 5 6 7 8 9 0   9 0 1 2 3 4 5 6

Author Judith Graham
Editor Libby Russell
Series designer Lynne Joesbury
Designer Louise Belcher
Illustrations Caroline Binch
Cover illustration Caroline Binch

Designed using Aldus Pagemaker

British Library Cataloguing-in-Publication Data
A catalogue record for this book is available
from the British Library.

ISBN 0-590-53731-8

ACKNOWLEDGEMENTS

Frances Lincoln Limited for the use of
illustrations and text from *Amazing Grace* by
Mary Hoffman © 1991 Text, Mary Hoffman
© 1991 Illustration, Caroline Binch (1991, Frances
Lincoln Ltd).

INTRODUCTION

Amazing Grace
by Mary Hoffman and Caroline Binch

WHAT'S THE PLOT OF THE STORY?

This is the story of Grace, a talented girl who loves acting out stories. Her class is going to perform Peter Pan but some of her class mates think Grace is not right for the main part. With the support of her mother and grandmother, Grace proves that 'when she puts her mind to it she can do anything'.

WHAT'S SO GOOD ABOUT THIS BOOK?

Amazing Grace is a short book but full of important talking points. It refers to many stories, such as 'Aladdin' and 'Joan of Arc', that you may recognise.

ABOUT MARY HOFFMAN

Mary Hoffman is the author of over 40 books for children. She often writes about children who win through against the odds. There is another book about Grace, *Grace and Family*, in which Grace goes to visit her father in Africa.

ABOUT CAROLINE BINCH

Caroline Binch is the illustrator of this book, and her realistic and boldly coloured illustrations give a great feeling of character and movement. She has illustrated many books and, for the book *Gregory Cool*, she drew the illustrations and wrote the words.

Make-believe play

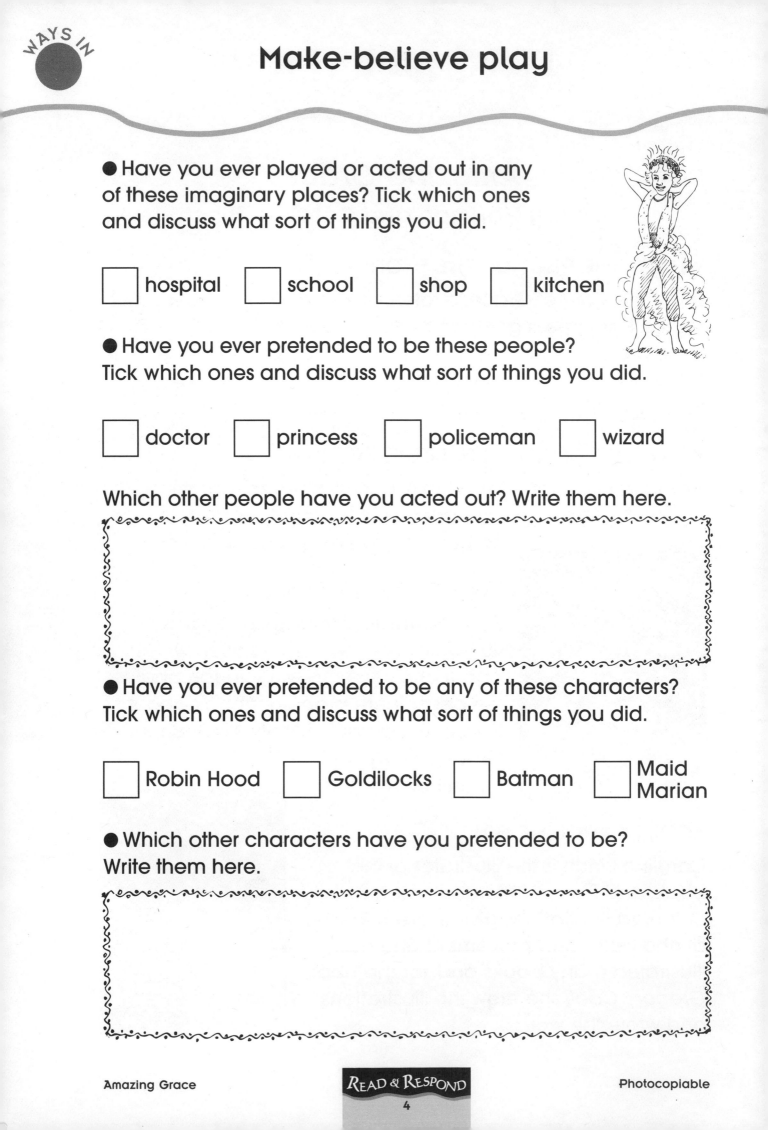

● Have you ever played or acted out in any of these imaginary places? Tick which ones and discuss what sort of things you did.

☐ hospital   ☐ school   ☐ shop   ☐ kitchen

● Have you ever pretended to be these people? Tick which ones and discuss what sort of things you did.

☐ doctor   ☐ princess   ☐ policeman   ☐ wizard

Which other people have you acted out? Write them here.

```



```

● Have you ever pretended to be any of these characters? Tick which ones and discuss what sort of things you did.

☐ Robin Hood   ☐ Goldilocks   ☐ Batman   ☐ Maid Marian

● Which other characters have you pretended to be? Write them here.

```



```

Reading the covers

● Look carefully at the front cover of the book – the title comes from a well-known song. You can probably guess that the girl in the picture is the 'Grace' of the title.

● Describe Grace to each other, using all the details in the picture.

● Look carefully at the back cover. Look first at the **picture** and discuss what you think the story will be about. Then write down your predictions. Remember the title of the book and your discussion of the front cover picture.

```
[blank box]
```

● Now read and discuss the **words** on the back cover and then answer the the following two questions:
Why is some of the writing put in inverted commas ("...")?
Why is some of the writing in *italic* writing?

● Now fill in these details about the book:

Title of book: _____

Main character: _____

Author: _____

Illustrator: _____

What the *Financial Times* said about it: _____

_____

Grace and her world of make-believe

Here are some of the props Grace uses in her make-believe games.

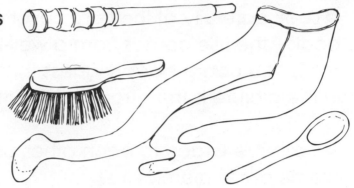

● Look at them carefully, decide what they are and then find them in the book.

● When you have done the above, fill in the sentences below.

Grace uses _____ to represent the spider's legs.

Grace uses _____ to represent the spider's head.

Grace uses _____ to represent the wooden horse's body.

Grace uses _____ to represent the horse's tail.

Grace uses _____ to represent a telescope.

Grace uses _____ to represent wild animals.

Grace uses _____ to represent a magic lamp.

Grace uses _____ and

_____ to represent a stethoscope.

Grace uses _____ to represent a hospital blanket.

"You can't be called Peter," said Raj. "That's a boy's name."

"You can't be Peter Pan," whispered Natalie.

"He wasn't black."

● Turn to the page where Grace's two class mates say these words to her. Why do Raj and Natalie, who seem to be Grace's friends, say these things which might upset her?

● Write your ideas below.

Raj and Natalie _____

_____

_____

● Now imagine that their teacher explains to Raj and Natalie that what they have said is not quite true and might have upset Grace. In groups of three, act out what the teacher says and how Raj and Natalie reply.

I want to tell you two something about acting and plays.

Grace's feelings

● Read up to the page where Grace gets home from school. Grace knows that she is a good actress. She knows that the auditions are still to come. So, why is she sad when she gets home?

● Write your ideas below.

Grace is sad because _____

_____

_____

_____

Before she talks to Ma and Nana about what happened, Grace decides to write her diary for the day.
● Finish Grace's diary entry.

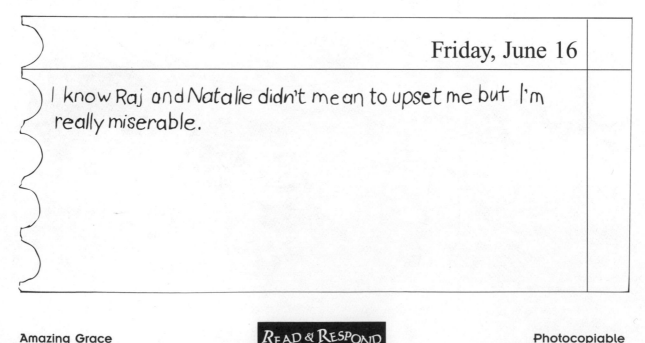

Friday, June 16

I know Raj and Natalie didn't mean to upset me but I'm really miserable.

Ma gets angry

● Read up to where Nana says: "You can be anything you want..." Why do you think Ma gets angry when Grace tells her what happened at school?

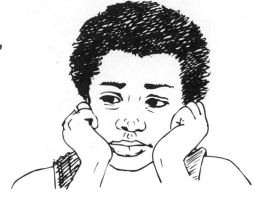

● Write your ideas below.

Ma gets angry because _____

_____

_____

● Imagine that later, when Grace has gone to bed, Ma and Nana have a long talk about what has happened and how they can help. Write their conversation. Set it out as a short play script – the first part has been done for you.

> Ma: *I think it's a downright shame that Grace comes home so sad because of what Natalie and Raj said.*
>
> Nana: *Now, now. I'm not so sure that Natalie and Raj understand some things.*

After the ballet

● Read up to the page where Grace pretends to be Juliet in the ballet. Why do you think Grace is more cheerful now?

● Write your ideas below.

Grace is more cheerful because _____

_____

_____

● Now imagine that before school begins on Monday morning, Grace tells Raj and Natalie all about her trip to the ballet with Nana. Grace does most of the talking because she wants to tell her friends about what effect the ballet had on her. Raj and Natalie ask questions and begin to realise how determined Grace is and that they might have been wrong saying that Grace could not play Peter Pan.

● In a group of three, act out their conversation.

Gaps in the text: **Peter Pan rehearsals**

● Read to the end of the book.

In *Amazing Grace* the author, Mary Hoffman, has left out some things that happen because she wants us to get to the important parts. One of the things she leaves out is the rehearsals of *Peter Pan*. But the rehearsals will have been very important to Grace!

● Write Grace's diary for the day when rehearsals begin. It has been started for you.

	Tuesday, June 20
Today, after the auditions yesterday, we began rehearsals for Peter Pan!	

Photocopiable

11

Amazing Grace

Words and pictures together tell the story

In a picture book like *Amazing Grace* the author does not have to *write* everything because she can leave the illustrator to *show* some things.

● Look at the picture of the classroom where the children are putting up their hands. When you have decided whether the information comes from the words or the pictures, tick the right box for the following sentences.

The name of the play is Peter Pan and two
of the children are called Raj and Natalie.
☐ Words
☐ Pictures

The children are sitting on the classroom floor.
☐ Words
☐ Pictures

Raj and Natalie are saying that
Grace cannot be Peter Pan.
☐ Words
☐ Pictures

One of the children in the class
has got her back to the teacher.
☐ Words
☐ Pictures

The teacher has told them that they
are going to do a play.
☐ Words
☐ Pictures

Raj and Natalie are sitting on either
side of Grace.
☐ Words
☐ Pictures

One boy is wearing a hat.
☐ Words
☐ Pictures

The auditions are going to be on the
following Monday.
☐ Words
☐ Pictures

The classroom has got children's
pictures on the walls.
☐ Words
☐ Pictures

Reflecting on reading

● Now you have read the story, look back at the prediction you made about the story before you read it. How close were your guesses?

● Remember how upset Grace was by Raj and Natalie. Is there anything that anybody could say or do to upset you about your hobby or interests? Write about it here.

● Who would cheer you up, like Grace's Nana cheered her up? What would they do to cheer you up? Write about it here.

The minor characters: **Grace's class teacher**

Grace's teacher is a minor character in the story. We do not see her (or it could be a him) in the illustrations. But we know that she is fair and that she lets her class help her make some decisions. We know this from what she *says* in the story and from what the story tells us she *does*.

● Re-read the book to help you fill in the spaces below. What does Grace's teacher *say* in the story which shows that she is fair?

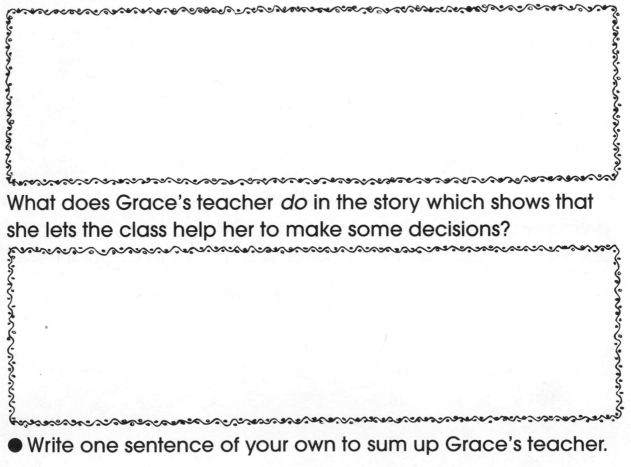

What does Grace's teacher *do* in the story which shows that she lets the class help her to make some decisions?

● Write one sentence of your own to sum up Grace's teacher.

_____

_____

● Read this description of Natalie.

Natalie is in the same class as Grace. She sits next to Grace so she is probably a friend. She has long brown wavy hair. Natalie thinks that Peter Pan is a white character in the play and that Grace cannot play the part. When she says this to Grace, she probably does not realise that she is upsetting her.

Natalie, like Grace, enjoys acting and she was chosen to play Wendy. At the auditions, she votes for Grace to have the part of Peter Pan. She watches her practising with a smile on her face and tells her that she is great.

● Now write about Raj, using everything that you read in the story and see in the illustrations.

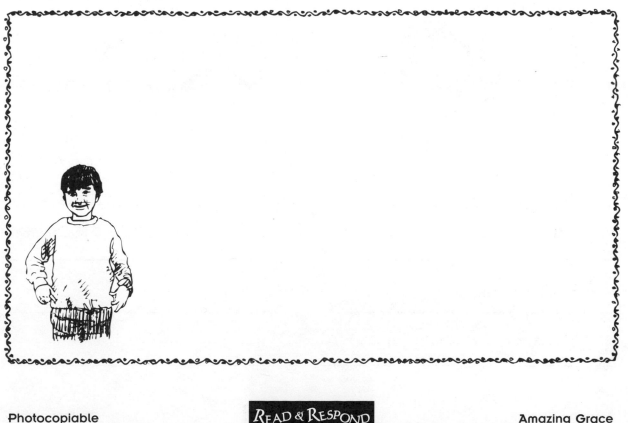

The major characters: Grace's Nana (1)

Grace's Nana is important in the story for lots of reasons.
● Under each of the pictures below, write a sentence saying what Nana is doing.

_____   _____

_____   _____

_____   _____

_____   _____

_____   _____

_____   _____

Amazing Grace      Photocopiable

● Imagine that Grace is grown-up and that she is a famous actress. When she is interviewed by a news reporter about her life, she says she would never have done anything if it had not been for her Nana. Write what she says in the finished report.

THE DAILY NEWS

FAMOUS ACTRESS
SAYS SHE OWES IT ALL TO HER NAN!

Grace _____,
the famous actress currently
appearing on stage in the
West End in

_____,
says that her grandmother
was the major influence on
her success.
"When I was a kid," she said,

"my Nana _____ _____

_____ _____

_____ _____

_____ _____

_____ _____

The major characters: Grace's Ma

Grace's Ma is not quite so important in the story as Nana but she is still a major character. The author tells us a lot about what she says and does, and the illustrator gives us four different pictures of her.

● Look carefully at these illustrations. Tick the words underneath that you think describe Ma at that moment. Use a dictionary to find the meanings of any words you don't know.

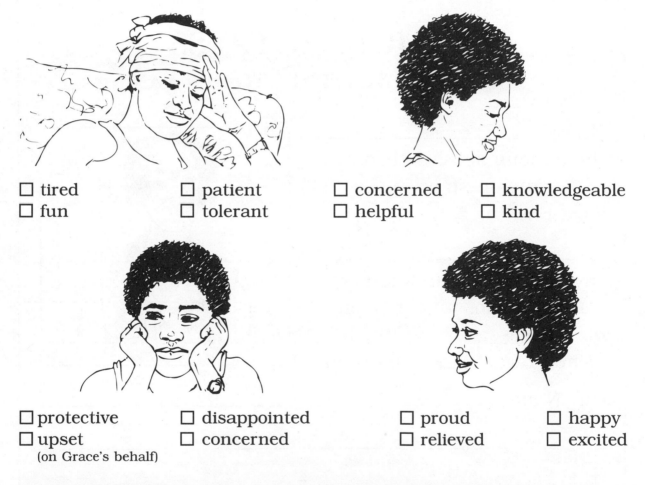

☐ tired   ☐ patient   ☐ concerned   ☐ knowledgeable
☐ fun   ☐ tolerant   ☐ helpful   ☐ kind

☐ protective   ☐ disappointed   ☐ proud   ☐ happy
☐ upset   ☐ concerned   ☐ relieved   ☐ excited
(on Grace's behalf)

● Now write one sentence to summarise Grace's Ma. If you can, write another sentence on the back of this sheet to say how she is different from Grace's Nana.

_____

_____

The major characters: Grace

Grace is the main character in the story. We see her in lots of different situations. We form an opinion of Grace's character from what she says and does, and from what other characters say about her.

Here are six words which describe her. Look up any words you are not sure of in a dictionary.

● After each one of the words, write the part of the story that leads us to form this opinion of Grace. The first one has been done for you.

Imaginative: _Grace uses all sorts of objects, like tights_
_____ _as props to help her act out the stories._

Ambitious: _____

_____

Determined: _____

_____

Sensitive: _____

_____

Active: _____

_____

Talented: _____

_____

The shape of the story

Amazing Grace follows a 'story shape' (or pattern) very similar to the shape of many other stories.

● Look at the chart below and make sure you understand it.

Opening: we are introduced to the main character. We are given details which are important to the story later on. We meet minor characters.

Important event: one particular event is described in detail. This part of a story often begins 'One day…' or 'Now…' or 'It so happened…'. The main character has to face a new situation.

Development: the main character tries to deal with the situation, sometimes with the help of other characters.

Ending: the main character triumphs.

● Now cut out the four sentences below and glue them in the right place in the chart above. Cut along all the dotted lines.

✂ -

Grace gets the part of Peter Pan and is a great success.

- -

Grace's class is going to put on a play but Raj and Natalie say Grace is wrong for the part of Peter Pan.

- -

Examples of Grace's love of acting out stories are given and we see that her Nana and Ma are loving and patient.

- -

Ma and Nana comfort Grace and her Nana takes her to the ballet. Grace gets back her confidence.

GRACE

Character and plot sums

Stories are not really like sums of course.
But without character and plot there is no story.
● Look at this 'sum':

Grace was brilliant at acting

+ She put her hand up to play the
part of Peter Pan in her school play.

= The story of *Amazing Grace*

● Can you add the missing line in the three 'sums' below?
Remember the line that you add will be about what the
character does.

Nana was very kind

+ _____

= The story of *Amazing Grace*

Grace loved the ballet
and was inspired by it

+ _____

= The story of *Amazing Grace*

Grace was determined and talented

+ _____

= The story of *Amazing Grace*

Indirect and direct speech

● Imagine that Grace writes the following in her diary:

> After the play was over, I felt so good that I told my Ma and Nana I felt as if I could fly all the way home. My Ma said that I probably could. Then my Nana said that if I put my mind to it I could do anything I wanted!

● Write the actual words that Ma, Nana and Grace said in their speech bubbles below. You can check your version by looking at the last page of the book.

You can do anything you want to

"You can be anything you want … if you put your mind to it."

● This is what Nana says to Grace. Do you think it's true?

● Think about the questions below and the story of Grace.
• Is determination enough to get you where you want to go?
• Does luck play a part?

• Does the faith and support of other people play a part?
• Do you think some people are born talented?
• Is talent enough on its own to get you where you want to go?

● Survey your class and see how many people think that: 'You can be anything you want if you put your mind to it'

Class survey

'You can be anything you want if you put your mind to it.'

Agree	
Disagree	
Don't know	

Grace's fund of stories

We see Grace acting out characters from the following stories:

Joan of Arc   Anansi
The Wooden Horse of Troy   Hannibal crossing the Alps
Long John Silver   Hiawatha
Mowgli   Dick Whittington
Aladdin   Peter Pan

Perhaps you know some of the stories.

● Read as many of them as you can. Choose one of the stories and re-read it until you know it very well. Can you retell it from memory? It will help if you think of its 'story shape'.

● Now practise retelling it.

● Imagine that Nana has taken photographs of Grace acting out some of the stories. She asks Grace about the photographs. Complete their conversation using details from the stories you have read and the illustrations from the book *Amazing Grace*.

Nana (with a photograph of Grace as Joan of Arc): Hey Grace! Come and see these photos. They're all of you playing. Look at this one. Are you leading your troops into battle?
Grace: That's me being Joan of Arc. They burnt me at the stake at the end of that game. Not really!

Nana: Oh, you've got my old black hat on and what a look on your face. You're really sulky!
Grace: Ha! That's me playing _____

_____

Nana: Here you are creeping through the jungle with Paw-Paw. There's some wild bears under a tree.

Grace: _____

_____

Nana: Now at least I can see this is a wooden elephant. Who are you here Grace?

Grace: _____

_____

Nana: And who's got her Mum's wellington boots on here?

Grace: _____

_____

Nana: Ah! I remember this time. I had to stick that parrot on your shoulder and tie your peg-leg on. Good thing you didn't fall off that chair.

Grace: _____

_____

Nana: Look at this! Amazing what you can do with a cardboard box.

Grace: _____

_____

Nana: Ah! I seem to remember you complained a bit when we had to scrub the paint off your face after this. Just look at Paw-Paw!

Grace: _____

_____

Nana: Hmm! Is that my best teapot?

Grace: _____

_____

Hot-seating Grace!

The school performance of *Peter Pan* is over.

● One of you take the part of Grace while the others quiz you about what happened since you first heard your class was going to put on the performance. Answer their questions in role as 'Grace'. More than one person can share the role if you prefer. Here are two questions to start you off.

> Grace, how did you feel when you auditioned for the part of Peter Pan?

> Grace, have you always enjoyed acting?

● Swap over roles part way through, so that everybody has a chance to answer in role as Grace.

USING THIS BOOK

HOW TO USE THIS BOOK

It is not intended that all children work through every activity in this book. However, if you plan so that groups and individuals work on different activities and then report back, the class will experience all the activities.
Ways in activities are for before the story is read. They explore the most accessible topic of the book – Grace's make-believe play, and aspects of the covers. Predictions are made at this stage.
Making sense activities are designed to ensure that key moments of the book are understood. Read through the whole of *Amazing Grace* initially, without stopping to do activities. Then revisit some or all of these key moments, using activities in this section.
Developing ideas activities encourage children to review the story and gain a wider perspective on it (for example: pages 14–19 tease out the features of both the major and minor characters).
Evaluation activity uses the drama technique of 'hot-seating'. One or more children take the role of characters in the book, and ask and answer questions put to them by the rest of the class. By this stage, the children should be able to use questions and answers which review and confirm their understanding of the whole book.

CLASSROOM MANAGEMENT AND SUPPORT

• Stage one – before children see the book, do the activity on page 4.
• Stage two – tackle page 5 as a class initially, showing the front and back covers to all the children, and then follow with individual work.

• Stage three – read the whole story to the class, at least twice. Aim for an uninterrupted first-time reading, then pause for comments during the second.
• Stage four – allow groups of at least three to work on the book, sharing further readings and moving on to pages 6–12 which require access to the book. These activities follow the events of the book, so if groups work on different activities, they should report back in order.

ACCESS TO THE BOOK ITSELF

Activities which require children to have access to the book are marked with the book icon.
   With careful planning, three copies of *Amazing Grace* would be just enough, depending on the size of your class and on whether you plan for some groups to work on text-dependent activities while others attempt activities which do not require access to the text.

SUGGESTED GROUPINGS

All activities can be flexibly approached to suit your classroom organisation. The table below suggests groupings.

	individual	small group	whole class
p 4		*	
p 5-6	*		*
p 7	*	*	
p 8	*		
p 9	*	*	
p 10	*	*	
p 11	*	*	
p 12	*	*	
p 13	*		
p 14	*		
p 15	*		
p 16-17	*		
p 18	*		
p 19	*		*
p 20	*	*	*
p 21	*	*	*
p 22	*	*	
p 23		*	*
p 24-25	*	*	*
p 26		*	*

LINKING ACTIVITIES

• The following activities could be linked:
page 6 and page 24; page 7 and pages 14–15; page 10 and pages 16–18; page 20 and page 21.
• The following activities follow a sequence and therefore provide coherence if worked on in numerical order:
pages 7–12; pages 14–19.

DIFFERENTIATION IN ACTIVITIES

Pages 4–6 have activites that are particularly suitable for less experienced readers and writers. The following activities are particularly suitable for more experienced readers and writers: page 9, page 18, page 19, page 21.

All activities (except page 5) can be undertaken without lengthy teacher input, though teachers will want to support and reinforce points with the class, groups and individuals where necessary (see the section called 'Prior teaching/background knowledge recommended' below).

EXTENSION ACTIVITIES

These activities can be used to support children who find the photocopiable activity too challenging, or to extend the work for children who complete it quickly. The activities range from being very broad in conception to very specific, and some are hugely ambitious. They are there for you to pick and choose from, according to the needs of your class and the time available to spend on the book.

TIME-SCALE

It is recommended that (with the class working in four groups or more) half an hour a day over a two week period is devoted to studying and reporting back on *Amazing Grace*. This will ensure that the children have experienced most of the activities, without exhausting enthusiasm for the book. The extension activities could take as much time again.

MATCHING THE BOOK TO THE CLASS

Amazing Grace is a multi-layered picture book and thus suitable for most children. It contains challenging themes and an absorbing crisis, and it raises thought-provoking issues.

The illustrations give details not referred to in the written text, giving readers pleasure as they discover them. The black family represented will interest most children.

Many of the activities are challenging but, with modelling and scaffolding, will be accessible to most children.

TEACHING POTENTIAL OF AMAZING GRACE
English

The activities, which meet National Curriculum requirements:
• develop understanding of plot, character, setting, themes, vocabulary, inference and deduction;
• offer opportunities to write and speak for varied purposes, in various genres and with a clear sense of audience;
• use improvisation and role-play.

Other curriculum areas

Because of the issues it raises, the book's potentially greatest contribution, apart from to English, is to PSE.

PRIOR TEACHING/BACKGROUND KNOWLEDGE RECOMMENDED

The children will need to be familiar with the following:
• structured small group discussion;
• dressing-up and make-believe play;
• predicting;
• role-playing conversation;
• writing diary entries, play scripts, newspaper interviews;
• using a dictionary;
• familiarity with the story grammar terms – 'opening', 'event', 'development', 'ending', 'character', 'plot';
• compiling a survey;
• retelling a story;
• writing direct and indirect speech;
• hot-seating a character.

If the children do not have any of the above background knowledge, the activities in this book could be used as an introduction to it.

For the extension activities, familiarity with letter layout, freeze-frames, writing frames, school reports, formal debates, dialect writing, theatre programmes and reviews would be helpful, though, not essential.

RECOMMENDED CLASSROOM RESOURCES FOR THE ACTIVITIES

For all activities, it is assumed that children will have writing materials in addition to the photocopiable pages. It is generally a good idea to provide a folder for each child to keep their completed work. Dictionaries should be made easily accessible.

Amazing Grace

Scissors and adhesive are needed for page 20. Extra copies of the chart from page 20 may be needed for page 24. Arrange for the stories listed on page 24 to be available for the children. Knowledge of these stories enhances their reading of *Amazing Grace*, but is not essential in order to understand the book. However, it *is* important that children know the story of Peter Pan.

FURTHER USEFUL RESOURCES

A tape recorder would be useful for activities where you may wish to record a discussion, or where children are unable to attempt the writing suggested.

Amazing Grace exists in several bilingual versions – Gujurati, Vietnamese, Turkish, Punjabi, Chinese, Bengali, Urdu and Arabic – all published by Magi Publications, London. A video version is produced by Weston Woods. No cassette version is currently available (children might like to make one of their own).

BOOKS USEFUL FOR WIDER READING

Books by Mary Hoffman

Ip Dip Sky Blue, ed. Mary Hoffman (Young Lions)
Dracula's Daughter (Heinemann)
Song of the Earth, illustrated by Jane Ray (Orion)
Grace & Family, illustrated by Caroline Binch (Frances Lincoln Limited)
Trace in Space (Hodder)
Special Powers (Hodder)

Picture books illustrated by Caroline Binch

Hue Boy, R P Mitchell (Gollancz)
Gregory Cool, Caroline Binch (Frances Lincoln Limited)
Grace & Family, Mary Hoffman (Frances Lincoln Limited)

Poetry *(particularly multi-cultural)*

Classic Poems to Read Aloud, ed. James Berry, illustrated by James Mayhew (Kingfisher)
No Hickory No Dickory No Dock, John Agard and Grace Nichols, illustrated by Penny Dann (Viking)
Can I buy a Slice of Sky? ed. Grace Nichols, illustrated by Liz Thomas (Blackie)

Picture books *(black families)*

Celebration Song, James Berry, illustrated by Louise Brierley (Hamish Hamilton)
So Much, Trish Cooke, illustrated by Helen Oxenbury (Walker)
Handa's Surprise, Eileen Browne (Walker)
Whistle for Willie, Ezra Jack Keats (Bodley Head)
(N.B. The titles by Isadora and Keats fit into the category below too.)

Picture books *(thematically linked – characters demonstrate determination or deal with disappointment)*

Michael, Tony Ross (Andersen)
The Iron Needle, Amanda Harvey (Macmillan)
Beware, Beware, Susan Hill, illustrated by Angela Barrett (Walker)
Rosalee and the Great Fire of London, Catherine Brighton (Cape)
The Whales' Song, Dyan Sheldon, illustrated by Gary Blythe (Hutchinson)
Alfie Gets in First and *Dogger*, Shirley Hughes (Bodley Head)
Dear Greenpeace, Simon James (Walker)
Leila, Sue Alexander, illustrated by Georges Lemoine (Hamish Hamilton)
Jump, Michelle Magorian, illustrated by Jan Ormerod (Walker)

Picture books *(thematically linked – putting on a play)*

The Nativity Play, Nick Butterworth and Mick Inkpen (Hodder & Stoughton)

TEACHERS' NOTES

SECTION ONE:
WAYS IN (PAGES 4–5)

MAKE-BELIEVE PLAY (FOR BEFORE THE BOOK HAS BEEN READ OR SEEN)

Aim: to relate a theme of the story to children's first-hand experience.

Teaching points: make-believe play usually revolves around settings, taking on the role of another person or taking the part of a character from a well-known story. Gender issues may be significant; there may be roles that children refuse to play.

Extensions: • Groups can be asked to report back to the whole class. • List on a flip chart other imaginary places, characters, stories that children invent for their play. • Talk through the role of props. • Provide dressing-up clothes to encourage make-believe play. • Discuss whether a person's colour or gender should limit the parts that can be played. • Make links between make-believe play and theatre. • Invite accounts of plays children might have been in and their experiences of being auditioned, rehearsing, learning lines, costumes, make-up, scenery, programmes, the big night, reviews, and so on.

THE FRONT AND BACK COVERS

Aims: to build up anticipation and predictions of story; to establish concept of main character, author and illustrator; to make deductions from the illustrations; to understand the role of other writing on the back cover.

Teaching points: key interest should be in the word 'amazing' and in the illustrations of the child. These details should guide the predictions made. Ensure that children realise that, at this stage, no-one can be accurate in their predictions. Discuss the role of book reviews and awards and ensure that any terms used are familiar to the class (such as: inverted commas, italic, publication and publish). Be prepared for queries about all aspects of the cover such as, what the ISBN number is for.

Extensions: • A display of picture books could be mounted where the main character is pictured on the front and/or is named in the title. • A contrasting set where the main character is not prominent could also be mounted. • Children could draw each other as if for front covers of books. • Discussion of the four title-page illustrations will reveal further clues to the story and refine children's predictions. (N.B. Grace's dressing-up clothes 'break through the frame' which draws our attention to what is significant.) • Children could draw more pictures of Grace in dressing-up clothes.

SECTION TWO:
MAKING SENSE (PAGES 6–12)

Aims: to encourage close reading, lateral thinking and deduction; to consider earlier predictions; to relate the book to own experience; to clarify areas beyond experience; to empathise with various situations, predicaments and feelings; to fill in textual 'gaps' to aid understanding; to analyse the different contributions of words and pictures.

Teaching points: for page 6, the props are: stockings, a soft hat, a cardboard box, a hand brush, a chair leg, teddy bears, a tea pot, a wooden spoon and tubing, a dressing gown. Pages 7 to 9 may require teacher intervention if the material is sensitive. Page 9 requires familiarity with play script layout. Page 12 requires the following explanation about words and pictures:

Four things that pictures show very well are:
1) what the characters' clothes and facial features look like;
2) what the characters are doing;
3) what the characters are feeling;
4) what the places look like.

Four things that are best done with words are:
1) what things and people are called;
2) what people are saying or thinking;
3) when things happen;
4) what happened earlier or will happen later.

The following words need to be understood, but may be deduced from context: 'props', 'represent', 'stethoscope' (page 6), 'auditions' (page 8), 'play script' (page 9), diary 'entries' (page 8) and 'rehearsals' (page 11).

Extensions: • Page 6 could be reversed so that the props are given (see list above) and what they represent has to be named. Both lists could be added to by finding further examples in the illustrations. • Page 7 could be approached as a letter of apology to Grace from Raj and Natalie. • Page 9 could include a telephone conversation, with Nana asking Rosalie's Granny for ballet tickets and explaining why. • Page 11 could include further diary entries to do with the performance of the ballet *Romeo and Juliet* and the school performance of *Peter Pan*. These are further 'gaps in the text' which experienced readers are able to fill easily; it is important to explain to children that we must take certain things as 'given' and jump over the gaps.
• Page 12 could be modelled initially with the whole class, using a different picture from the book, such as Grace pretending to be a doctor.

Amazing Grace

READ & RESPOND

• Children can be encouraged to use what they have learned from this activity in their own illustrated writing. • Depending on interest and opportunity, children could be encouraged to: dress up and use makeshift props; research the history of pantomime; draw each other in costume; inspect and browse through diaries and published play scripts; enact the play scripts they have created (or role-play before writing anything); visit a theatre rehearsal and/or attend a performance. • Going to the ballet was a turning point for Grace and individuals in the class may have comparable turning points to share with each other.

SECTION THREE:
DEVELOPING IDEAS (PAGES 13–25)

AFTER THE FIRST READINGS: REFLECTIONS (PAGE 13)
Aims: to note the distance between first predictions and informed reflections; to relate a second theme of the book to personal experience.
Teaching points: it is important that children do not worry if their early predictions were wide of the mark. Class discussion could centre on what could reasonably have been predicted and what would have been impossible to predict. Commend those children who relate their predictions to what is observable in illustration and text, and to what they know from their reading of other narratives. The writing task where being upset and being comforted is explored may need teacher support – children might prefer to write about a hypothetical experience rather than an actual one.
Extensions: • Children may wish to draw out and reflect on several other issues of personal importance prompted by the story, for example: hobbies, outings, friends, racism. • Encourage links with other books with similar themes. • Children could collect, write down and display examples of things that adults say to them to cheer them up, such as: 'Come on! Smile! It may never happen!' • They could write a poem of these sayings (see Michael Rosen's 'Things My Father Says' in *Mind Your Own Business* [Andre Deutsch]).

CHARACTERS (PAGES 14–19)
Aims: to consider the role of minor and major characters, how character is created by author and illustrator, characters' point of view; to develop perspective on character; to develop a vocabulary for describing character.
Teaching points: deducing character based on actions, speech and (in a picture book) illustration is important here. The class needs

to know the book really well at this stage. Page 17 may need teacher modelling and appropriate interviews in magazines could be examined. Dictionaries need to be available for pages 18 and 19.
Extensions: • The children could write Grace's school report. • Role-play between major and minor characters (for example: discussing the school performance of *Peter Pan*) while preserving character traits. • Make freeze-frame cameos of Grace with her Ma and Nana. • Further activities could be undertaken where different characters reflect, for example: Nana might write a letter about Grace to her relations in Trinidad or talk on the telephone to Rosalie's grandmother.

PLOT (PAGES 20 AND 21)
Aims: to appreciate the traditional story shape of *Amazing Grace*; to see the relationship between plot and character.
Teaching points: activities on story shape will need teacher explanation if no work has been done on this aspect of literature before. The lines which complete the sums (on page 21) could be: 'She took Grace to the ballet'; 'She cheered up and got the part in the audition'; 'She was a great success in the play'.
Extensions: • Any traditional story (such as, 'Cinderella') could be analysed in terms of its story shape. • Further texts where plot and character are intimately interconnected could be read, for example, *Michael,* by Tony Ross (Andersen Press) or *Mufaro's Beautiful Daughters* by John Steptoe (Hamish Hamilton). • Further 'sums' could be invented by the class.

INDIRECT AND DIRECT SPEECH (PAGE 22)
Aim: to consider how the author conveys both direct and indirect speech in her writing.
Teaching point: if work on the layout of speech has not been taught before, this activity will need teacher input.
Extensions: • Any section of direct speech in the book could be examined for how speech is represented: speech marks, new line for new speaker, punctuation within speech marks and so on. • This direct speech can be rewritten as indirect speech. • Indirect speech – the examples in the book are: 'Grace could persuade her Ma and Nana to join in'; 'Her teacher said they were going to do the play of Peter Pan'; 'Nana told Grace they were going out' – could be converted into direct speech. • The dialect in Nana's speech (there are four examples in the book) could be discussed. This needs to be tackled with a thoughtful, linguistic approach. It would not be helpful to turn the dialect into standard nor to convey any judgements. • Children could be

encouraged to use dialect in their own writing (John Agard and Grace Nichols have many dialect poems in their collections – see the recommended resources section on page 29).

THEME – 'YOU CAN DO ANYTHING YOU WANT TO' (PAGE 23)

Aims: to reflect on the main theme of the book; to debate the issue of determination; to produce a class survey.

Teaching point: the use of a discussion writing frame may help the organisation of ideas here. The headings could be the following:

There is a lot of argument about...;
The people who agree with this idea claim that...;
They also argue that...;
A further point they make is...;
However there are also strong arguments against these views. I believe that...;
Another counter argument is...;
Furthermore...;
After looking at the different points of view and the evidence for them, I think...

(Lewis, M & Wray, D *Developing Children's Non-Fiction Writing* [1995] Scholastic).

Extensions: • A formal debate could be attempted on the motion: 'Is determination enough?' • The class survey results could be put onto a computer.

GRACE'S FUND OF STORIES (PAGES 24–25)

Aims: to read some of Grace's favourite stories and choose one to retell, preserving story shape (see page 20); to record key points from several stories.

Teaching points: children need to be encouraged to retell without notes, keeping the visual images in their mind clear and the story line flowing, rather than remembering the exact words. Use copies of a 'story shape' from page 20 if necessary.

If the Nana/Grace conversation requires too much prior knowledge or research for the time available, groups or individuals could take one 'photograph' each and then report back to the class.

Extensions: • Follow-up work on the stories could include: retelling the story in modern times; retelling from a character's viewpoint; adding incidents; changing the ending; hot-seating the teller in role; presenting it as a play.
• Researching the stories could lead to comparisons of different versions. • Make a display of the stories stressing the different countries of origin.

SECTION FOUR: EVALUATION (PAGE 26)

HOT-SEATING GRACE AT THE END OF THE SHOW

Aim: to revisit the whole book.

Teaching points: asking and answering of questions in role gives the children the opportunity to reflect on the whole story. It also encourages insights into the character's emotional life. The teacher may need to model open questions that will elicit fuller answers.

Extensions: • Other characters from the book can be put in the hot-seat – this should bring out alternative perspectives. • The class could make a theatre programme for the performance of *Peter Pan*, using a computer (this would have even more relevance if the class could actually put on the play). A programme usually includes: the title of the ballet/play/pantomime; the author (writer) of the story; the composer of the music; the choreographer (if it is a ballet); when the ballet or play was first performed; the director; the costume designer; the scenery designer; the lighting engineer; the name of the company who are dancing or acting; the name of the orchestra; the conductor; a cast list; the acts and scenes of the ballet or play; a summary of the story; pictures and biographies of the cast. It takes a long time to prepare programmes and often, if they have advertisements in them too, they end up as little books. • A review of the performance could be written, based on actual newspaper reviews. These usually include: a little history of the play or ballet; a short summary of the story; a mention of how well the main actors or dancers performed; how well it was directed overall; how well the rest of the cast did; how the audience reacted.

Amazing Grace